For

These writings are pieces of prose inspired by my travels and my livings. They are not a form of proselytizing or preaching. Nor should anything in the first person necessarily be considered opinion.

They are gathered from a wide range of experiences, often involving others. Some of these people have been complete strangers. Some have been brief acquaintances. Some pieces have been compiled from discussions with close friends and guides, from both the inner realm and the outer world. Some occurred in actuality and some are entirely imagined. And some have come from romantic relationships.

The idea to write in this way resulted from an impasse between two of my passions: writing poetry and reading great literature. I am very much at home writing poetry but not willing to write literature. I've hardly read any other poetry but mine and yet devour works of prose. At various points, I found myself needing to express something that poetry could not do justice to, but I did not have the patience to craft and develop a working plot, set of characters, and setting. What resulted were brief expressions crafted linearly but without the accompanying backdrop that escorts a literary work.

I will not make any demands on the reader, but I do hope that you will attempt to stay open and allow these pieces to make an impression. Most of these moments correspond in some way to an experience of mine. As such, it is understandable that a stranger may find it difficult to relate to them. But I also believe that each sentence has the ability to resonate with any individual to some meaningful degree.

Observe what happens as you read, what comes to mind; what feelings arise; what thoughts; what wonder? Let them be a catalyst for your own exploration about life, love, truth, and wonder and your relationship to them. Feel free to write your own thoughts or reflections in the space below the passages. Try to interpret a meaning, but a meaning that relates to your own knowing and understanding, and not just to what you think I may be trying to say.
It has been said that truth charms. I challenge you to discover the validity of that claim. I desire for others to discover what these words may point to, and hope you are charmed in the process.

Mark Herbert Zimmermann

To the ineffable

And Let It Remain

"Is there a question I should be asking?"

"No."

"Then tell me about yourself. Where is the darkness?"

"There is no darkness here, only the eternity of the moment, the song below the waves that no one can hear since the sea sings above them. You are looking for the vastness past the horizon, but you will have to give up your sight to see it."

And he realized that any woman's love would never be enough; that he would never be satisfied with the love of a woman if he was unable to feel compassion for himself; that such a love, no matter how strong, could never be trusted so long as he failed to believe he was anything worth loving.

"The island of my life, it's the island of my dreams, the island I've been stranded on my whole life. Was I exiled? No. Nor did I strand myself. I merely fell in with the waves of the cosmic ocean, drifting afloat its mystical currents in an undying rhythm of grace and tranquility, until it washed me up upon the shores of the life discernment. I've been told it was for the sake of a 'wider' view."

They lay there talking of the future, of the prospect of parting. At the possibility of being without each other, their bodies became lifeless, like two corpses; they became like bags of sand. Their eyes lost the sparkle that was so prevalent between them: hers, from the thought of being without him; his, from seeing the glow that normally lit her face momentarily dissipate and vanish from her sight.

He thought of how all this was just a challenge, that what he was feeling was no fault of hers, that what he knew was love; that it was meant to overcome. He thought of his failings, how she inadvertently brought out what he needed to confront about himself, not so it would destroy their love but strengthen it.

He thought about the optimism he had at that time concerning new beginnings. He wondered if he was wrong for having it then; he wondered if it was wrong to want it now. That he desired either the past or optimism itself, he did not know.

He felt buried by the present moment and was uncertain what it meant. It involved feeling and being comfortable with the past, though it made him want to disappear from the present; it made him accepting and happy that in the present he was able to be so at home, at peace with his memories and comfortable with the person he had come to be. He thought about this contradiction: loving one's past from the present moment, loving the present because of it, but desiring to escape to the past nonetheless.

He had chanced to utter things that he instantly regretted, that he knew he never meant, words that merely spoke themselves – that is language sometimes.

He had seen her eyes close. He saw she had lost herself in a possibility, a possibility his words had only suggested, but not foretold: that he might get to a point where he could not stand her – something he immediately said would never happen. But the possibility had been spoken, and people live in possibility.

He felt she was not open to how much he hurt from having wounded her, of how helpless he felt in trying to make her feel better. He knew of nothing else he could do.

He told her he wanted to close himself off from her, but she said she would not let him. She got up and came to embrace him. For a moment he remained obstinate, but her words had been magic, and he gave up at the realization that here was a woman so willing to plunge to the depths of his emotions, to approach the door to his soul, and to walk in, to march in.

"Haven't you wished to go back to her and find out more about your future?" she asked.

"Sometimes, but I also feel that if I were to ask myself real hard, if I just looked inside real close, then my heart would tell me the answer to any of my questions. All people have this ability."

He thought about that question: "Would you not be disappointed if all your possessions became lost?" Of course, at the thought of such a prospect he certainly was not excited. He lifted his head and thought – it was a thought that sprang forth from a feeling, like a sapling from the soil: "No. I am more than that. I am more than my possessions." Simultaneously, he knew it was because he thought this way that possessions would always be bountiful. But then, another thought came: "If I don't need them then why do I have them?" What concerned him were the hard copies of his writings, writings he knew he cherished. But he could answer his own question, instantly and intuitively, "Because other people need them, not I. Is that true?"

He returned from class and stepped through the doorway into his room, but when he closed the door, he simply stopped and stood there; he could not move, he could only think. His thoughts had been with him the entire length of the walk back; they had taken steps with him. Now, upon reaching his room, they induced paralysis.

"I love, but it hurts" he thought. It hurt because the love he felt was colored by thoughts of rejection; the woman he loved was torn and could not commit to him. He was falling for a woman who wouldn't accept him, though she was very much in love herself.

The thought then arose, a thought on the inevitability of his love and the futility of denying his ability to give it: "I love her, and there's no getting around this feeling, whether she chooses to love me or not. If I don't choose to love her, regardless of the pain I may end up feeling, I'll be burdened with a lie, and the heavy weight of trying to protect myself." He paused…. "I choose to love her then! No matter what pain I feel."

All of this had occurred in his mind. When the decision to love her came to life, it manifested in an instant, owing to some great feeling that swelled up from inside. At that moment, he felt relieved. He knew it was a momentous step, but still, he underestimated what this moment meant for his life. For in choosing to love over a concern for his own fears of loss, he had surrendered to something greater than himself and let go of the defenses that keep a person from being able to commit fully to the divine. This was a moment when the door to his heart opened up, though it didn't hinge open as much as completely vanishing.

This all happened, not because he chose to love one woman specifically, but because he chose love over his own fears. He did not choose a woman as much as he chose love itself, and for that, it would make all the difference in his life.

He wanted to stay mad. He wanted to be mad at her because he wanted an excuse to reject her, and he wanted to reject her so she could never reject him. He had never been able to love himself, and thus he had inadvertently rejected himself as someone not worth loving. The thought of her rejection was therefore inevitable.

The great secret to living lies in nurturing that infinitesimal moment between being aware and knowing; before having to box an experience away into the mind, maintaining a state of presence with the great messengers of life.

"This situation and these circumstances haven't been about love or a relationship," he thought. "As such, my pain and suffering have not been because of her or the result of the challenges in our love. It has all been about transformation achieved through self-understanding and acceptance. This is a play we've been given to perform, and I must not confuse the actions for people, people who induce cause to effect by the desire of their wills. That is a job for the Fates; it is what God does, and we must not take out our frustrations personally on each other. We've merely been put in this situation with each other to realize something important about ourselves."

"Anything worth loving is worth suffering for."

...but first he had to be afraid, he had to let go of fear in order to feel fear; he had to love her without fear in order to feel the fear that he needed to confront; and he confronted it by letting go, not through guilt or any kind of guile, but through the realization that he was worthy of the ability to surrender.

At first, she thought nothing of knowing she would see him again. She knew her class was after his, but in her estimation, she counted up those brief seconds to a passing irrelevancy. But now the confidence in her ability to remain distant became a casualty in her struggle to hold back the feelings resulting from having him gone from her life. She found herself looking forward to seeing him for those few seconds. She wanted to own those few seconds tyrannically for the sake of fueling a desire to be with him, a desire she still felt burning in her soul, a desire she hated.

He got up and began packing his things. He kept his eye on her, hoping to meet her glance and tell her how beautiful she was. But her head stayed down as she read her book. Now his things were packed, but he didn't yet walk away. Now he stayed there, biding his time, pretending to fumble around in his pack, trying to appear like he was organizing it; waiting to meet her eyes. But her head stayed down, and she remained a stranger to him.

She had tried to get over him through force of will. That is, her act had not been spurred by a change of feeling over how she was in love. Instead, a rationalization had convinced her that separating was the best option for the future. Yet the cost of her reasoning and determination to see it through was the loss of an intimate connection she had to her own feelings, feelings that knew the truth of what was special to her heart, where the thunder that defined her love was still booming.

"Yes, but where is your childhood now?"

"I have a sneaking suspicion that most of us act only to avoid a confrontation with the fear we have that life, in its seeming finitude, is meaningless. At the end of life, all we appear to show is the amount of distance we've put between our illusions of having made something permanent out of impermanence along with the energy we've spent in trying to convince ourselves that things could in fact have never been different from how we perceived it all."

She had asserted that she knew what she wanted, so confidently, in fact, that she failed to consider the reality of its meaning. Moreover, she had failed to consider the inherent challenges to obtaining what she wanted. The challenges were now facing her, and they were causing her to doubt what she wanted. Yet in truth, what she wanted was still what she longed for, but it was feelings of pain and discomfort associated with having to overcome the challenges to gaining what her heart desired that made her doubt herself.

He adamantly asserted who he was and clung to it so as to be done experiencing the inevitable effects of change as he engaged with the world, a world with the propensity to shatter the will of any person determined to make it indissoluble. And so, as the currents of time flowed to erode the ground before him, he stood on the shore, intent on believing the currents would cease or that his will represented the very waves themselves.

That moment where one is able to truly love oneself; all the strength that comes with it; the incredible power gained from no longer needing to be affirmed through anyone; the limitless opportunities in choosing who one is going to love, who one is going to devote one's life too; being so affirmed by one's self that there is no fear in reaching out to others because there is nothing another person can do to dispel the sense of love one feels. Yes, he felt these things, but could he act on them?

"Try not to worry about that. Do what you want. Almost everyone will end up making a living," he said. "But only a rare few will make living meaningful."

What hurt most was realizing he still loved her, even though she refused to talk to him or even acknowledge his existence.

From where he sat, there was movement, a sound and a whisper trying to change itself, with hills from where he watched the trees sway, and bend with the wind; his soul in sync with their motion, and thought becoming something else; thought that fell to becoming, to existing absolute. He felt nothing wanted to be the same as he felt this nothing real. He felt the pulse of life, and knew death would not change a thing.

He lay on the bed, at peace with doing nothing. During such moments, it was important for him to find comfort in doing nothing, in doing nothing but being. For here he felt he had hit on one of the secrets of life: to be comfortable with doing nothing. This was not being lazy, far from it. Indeed, he had learned from watching people from the "baby boomer generation" how hard it was to do nothing, and had come to feel that it was those people working constantly, unable to ever truly rest and take time to enjoy being alive, unable to enjoy life itself; perhaps those people who thought being an incessant worker meant being virtuous were truly lazy. To him they were the laziest of people for they were too lazy to stop and take in the pure essence of life; life with its good and bad, with its perplexity, and the existential anxiety that came with wondering about it all.

Such people had busied themselves with the belief that existing meant doing and doing meant being. But all he ever learned from watching such people, with their incessant activity, was that their drive to stay busy was at heart nothing more than a determination to avoid some inevitable reality about life, and that they were merely trying to escape some unavoidable day when an individual is no longer physically fit enough to occupy his or her thoughts through labor; with the inevitable reality of being feeble, bed ridden, and stuck relatively handicapped with a whole world of doubt concerning the point of life, four cornering the space and time left to existence. "No, better to face any hard truths now," he thought.

But for now, happiness lay inside of her, dormant, like a sleeping volcano, waiting to erupt at a time when the worst of her fears had been confronted along with the agonizing pain and secret shame that came from being unable to ignore certain questions about the purpose of life and of existence itself.

For here was an old woman, wise, but wise not from collecting knowledge, from travelling to foreign lands, or from philosophizing. Here was a woman who found wisdom by not trying to find it at all, a woman who humbled her self to the quiet desperation that most everybody else struggles throughout life in vain to overcome; such people rarely know what they are getting into when they do so. Here was a woman who survived the rip tide of life, not by trying to swim back to shore, but by surrendering to its power. This power was not entirely that of society itself, but that naked power that seemed to make something like society inevitable.

She found wisdom through living honestly through herself. She acknowledged that in her youth she had been too afraid to do anything that strayed from what was expected of her. She lived honestly with this in heart, and from it sprouted an integrity that was able to see the world for what it was and not for what people deluded themselves into believing it should be.

She continued to wash the dishes as they talked. After letting out a few feigned sighs, her grandson looked at her and smiled. She paused from washing the dishes, looked right at her grandson and said, "Honey, you're not ready."

She had uttered something similar to her soon to be daughter-in-law 30 years prior, knowing that her son, the man to whom this woman was to be wedded, was still too enmeshed in a world wandering from groups of friends to groups of friends, and from one woman to another.

But the wandering of her grandson did not involve wandering from woman to woman or engaging with groups of friends still content to do nothing but party. His was a wandering from place to place, from culture to culture, from foreign land to foreign land, all with the desire to feel life as much as was possible, a type of wandering she knew made the idea of settling down a foolhardy endeavor.

"No, the problem is not that you feel depressed or sad at times. The problem is that you think it is a bad thing to feel such things at all. You measure yourself against the rest of society where everyone wears a false and ridiculous smile, all because they are afraid to feel life in its entirety, and so you think yourself something shameful and base by comparison."

He sat there listening with his head down, feeling the urge to respond struggle with the urge to remain silent.

"You want your peace, I know, but it doesn't lie in any kind of dishonesty with yourself."

"Before I rush to do this: Am I doing it out of boredom, in order to escape the monotony of life, or am I doing it out of some genuine passion to learn about the world, and get in touch with some undiscovered aspect of it?"

In Sufism, there is a Turkish word, *hüzün*, which is used to describe a melancholic feeling that Sufis feel from being unable to get any closer to God. He felt this same melancholy when it came to trying to take in the world through his senses. For him, no matter how hard and with what concentration he tried to taste, feel, smell, hear, and see the world, he could never quite transport as deeply as he felt was possible. Of course, he would transport to certain places: a sip of tea would take him to misty hill-tops with endless rows of tea trees; a piece of chocolate might take him to some tropical climate where he would sit protected from the intensity of the sun's heat; the smell of the ocean might take him underwater to swim with beautifully colored fish. All of this and yet he wanted more, to get closer. He wanted to be these things because deep within the recesses of his feelings he felt a part of him was all things, and all things him.

They sat at the dinner table. She brought her hands together saying, "Thank you for this."

"Who are you thanking?" her older sister asked.

"No one. I'm just thankful."

"Are you thanking God?" her father asked.

"No. I don't know whom I'm thanking, and it doesn't seem to matter. I'm just thankful, I'm thankful there is food when so many children are starving. I'm thankful I have a home, and I'm thankful I don't have to sleep out in the cold at night. I'm just thankful."

The rest of the family sat listening, chewing their food with their heads low to their plates, but with eyes up, unable to resist being moved by what she was saying, encouraged by their own curiosity."

"Well you have to be thanking someone. It doesn't make sense otherwise," her sister retorted.

"Yes, it makes perfect sense!" I realize that for some unknown reason I have things that others don't and I'm happy and grateful for it."

"But that's a prayer you said!"

"No it's not! And even if it is, it is still true!"

"That's ridiculous!"

"And you're stupid!"

One of the things he was most attracted to was her sense of style; she did not wear clothes that showed off her body, almost as if on purpose, though she would probably never admit such a thing. It wasn't that she lacked the necessary features for wearing "sexy" clothes. When she did wear a dress, one that was always classy with just the right amount of sex appeal, she was perfectly at home, though one could tell at times that she could be mildly uncomfortable as well; again, something she would probably never admit.

All this attracted him because she was a woman who one found attractive and charming by the force of her personality. It was the confidence and grace with which she conversed with you, it was the patient and caring way she watched and listened to what you had to say, and it was the beautiful and charming way she flexed her large dimples when she smiled that made everyone who ever interacted with her, both male and female, instantly fall in love with her; something she would never believe but was entirely true.

He sat down to write, thinking of her and how it felt to make love. He thought about trying capture those feelings in words, for a part of him could not resist the urge to put the past onto paper and somehow believe that by doing so he was bringing the past back to life, as if such a thing was possible. He looked down at the paper, his pen hovering close to the page. He lost himself in stare, and took his head up from the paper…

He could not do it. He wanted to preserve those memories and honor the feelings associated with them. He did not want to bastardize those moments, for although he knew he was a fine writer, he was too aware that his words could never do their lovemaking justice. He dropped his pen onto the desk and looked out the side window to see two birds sitting perched together in song… He wrote nothing the rest of the day.

"How come you've never asked me to choose between you?" she said.

"Because I feel that if our situation was easier and it came down to it that you would choose me."

What he said was the truth, but there was more. In his heart, he felt that she had chosen him, not because she had cheated on her boyfriend on separate occasions, as if cheating meant that deep down she couldn't possibly love him if she chose to do so, but because he had seen that look in her eyes when he stared at her. He knew how much she loved the way he would look into her eyes; it made her feel desired, like she was the only woman he saw. She knew that for him to look at anyone else this way would be as unnatural, unlikely, and undesirable as a bird wishing to give up its wings.

Her real name is irrelevant, but in his mind, he called her 'the black rose,' both for her black hair and for her stunning beauty, with eyes like caves. But not the part of the cave so distant from the opening that no light ever pierces it. It was more like that part of a cave where, as one goes deeper, one reaches that part where light will touch it for no more than a few steps. A cave is also an appropriate analogy, for it is a cave that contains dark recesses of space that no eye ever sees.

"Likewise, I will refrain from saying anything more of this woman, and will keep, like in a cave, my thoughts somewhere within the dark recesses of my mind, at the risk of otherwise falling victim to my vulnerabilities and vices."

"I'm obsessed with the color of this tea, a deep and rich amber color that appears to both refract and absorb the sun's light, a color that is very much a friend of the sun itself, as the latter affectionately shines its rays through my glass while I take another sip. These people drink tea all day even though the temperature is 90 degrees. How can I not love such a people?"

And so they continued to put off their final conversation, the last time, it was decided, they would talk to each other. They delayed, delayed, and delayed until they decided to have no conversation at all, that words would do little justice to what they were feeling, and that the unsaid would stay the more beautiful, and honor the truth better if it remained unspoken.

No man would deny the warmth and awe in recognizing the beauty of a woman unbeknownst to him as she shined forth with fresh and radiant light, like a morning sunrise. No one could dare retort that with so many beautiful women blessed with an infinite amount of tempting intricacies, there might be anything less than an endless search for beauty everlasting.

That we interpret love in many ways only adds to the commotion of our turbulent minds; cursed by our eyes and damned by the senses we use to govern our passions, we replace reason with beloved.

We see a woman, and her sight is a gasp of fresh air. We see her walk, and we become a prisoner. We watch her lips open, and feel with every delicate breath she takes that she is inhaling our soul. What bliss indeed!

Is it that we enjoy being slaves to such splendor, or do we simply loose our capacity to think? We become stranded, and thus we leave our spirits to the mercy of lust, pain, and desire. These feelings then become appealing in there own right, as an aftertaste of the divine.

He arrived back home that night, sat down, and wrote the following lines:

Your beauty brings forth a soft temperance to the calamity of life. In this, time stops, as base desires strain to catch up to the moment in passing, but they too, observe in reverence upon arrival. There is serenity here that envelops the senses in a state of awe, calm and soft like snowfall on a still winter's night. You have the proportions of symmetry that architects desire in their attempts at masterpiece, and your skin illuminates with such modesty, revealing a texture so delicate, that my eyes hesitate to blink.

He's like the fool who thinks he can forget his lover by avoiding those places that remind him of her the most, the places they frequented together, the places where they made love, those places where they spoke to each other with great affection; places where they laughed, cried, confessed, and opened up, not realizing that it only promotes and prolongs his suffering, not realizing that he carries the source of his suffering within, for in trying to deny and avoid the suffering associated with visiting these places, he only manages to transfer it to new areas, as if carrying a disease that is unknowingly being spread as he goes about living normally from day to day. Or, like air caught in a sealed plastic bag that he succeeds in only pushing from one corner of the bag to another until finally deciding to undo the bag and let the air out.

And so he quit the team. Most people, when they are in the middle of experiencing moments that will prove to be some of the most important in their lives, have no clue of the profundity to which they are bearing direct witness. And although he, too, did not know at that moment what this choice would mean, he did feel it, and was therefore able to take in some of the power and magnanimity of what was happening.

Later that evening, he told his father. His father was shocked and disappointed, asking, "Why?" and following that up with, "You're not a quitter, are you?"

But whereas his father saw quitting the team to mean "giving up," his son had saw it as "letting go," letting go of something that no longer gave him pleasure; letting go of the feeling that one was obligated to persevere when one had the ability to simply stop.

"Well, you might as well get a job," his father said, in a half serious tone, trying to suggest that such a thing was the only other option, an option his son never considered and, indeed, never followed through with for the remaining duration of his high school career.

In that moment, he thought about the meaning of life, but in this instance, he was not stirred by the question itself. By this time, he had ceased asking that question: "What is the meaning of life?" Instead, he gave way to his feelings, seeking the answer somewhere in the silence of subtle perception.

It was not that asking questions served no purpose; there were certainly times when such a question was poignant and necessary. But now he felt such a question already betrayed the possibility of an answer, for he knew that "What is the meaning of life?" was a question of the mind, and as such, could never give answer to what was essentially a sensation. No, the answer to such a question lay simply in opening up what was directly in front of him. He knew that silence held all the answers if one was patient and determined enough to listen.

"Then why love?"

"Love is the affirmation of one's connection to all things."

"You cannot love something entirely without embracing that thing's impermanence."

"It's Halloween; a person dresses up in a particular costume to play a certain role for the night. The night ends, but this person continues to wear the costume, even until the next morning, the next day, the next week… This is essentially what each one of us is doing. We all put on a particular identity, a persona, a costume, and we continue to wear and invest in it, even though it's not real, forgetting we can take it off."

The endless distractions: a glass of tea here, a cigarette there; a nap, a walk, an endless stretch of daydreams; songs, food, drinks, TV shows, movies; idle talk, video games, gossip. The restlessness that gives way to movement, the movement that gives way to restlessness, and somewhere, floating between, a stillness that seems ephemeral, but only because one tries to hold on to it.

Doesn't it bother you that you have to have sound all the time, that you can't sleep without music? Shouldn't it alarm you or anyone that you are unable to tolerate silence? What will happen when you're older, or on your deathbed? Won't silence catch up with you, chasing the very bones in your body as they begin to age and weaken? You'll fight the silence with your body through tensions that make your muscles strain as your bones crack. You'll come to love your decaying body because of the sounds emanating from its decrepitness, and you'll pass away telling your self there was no other way. You'll die screaming in your head with a voice that no one will ever hear.

He replayed that moment in his mind, right after they broke up; his final words before leaving: "If you feel breaking up is best for your future, then I support it, even at the cost of not having you."

Of course, it was the "right thing" to say, the noble, selfless, and loving thing to say, but he didn't really mean it, and so, it was the completely wrong thing to say.

He wanted to mean it, but in truth, he said such a thing only to hide his insecurities associated with losing a woman that he couldn't stand to be away from. He had tried to play it "cool" as if he couldn't be hurt, owing to some love he thought he had for himself, but it was a lie.

He had not reached such a point of self-love with himself then, but he was very close to such a point now, and so the memory of having so skillfully deceived himself only made him smile.

They stood in the open, in front of the airport security, holding each other in silence. It never occurred to him that this could be the last time he ever saw her. But that thought had now jumped into his mind, and it made him cry.

"No, no, no, you're with someone who loves you!"

He lay in bed, on his side, with his arm by his face, stretched over his head. From this angle, he could see the pulse in the vein of his arm. He watched and began staring at it drearily. Soon he was thinking of her, focusing on the beat, the pulsation. Before long, the beat became her breathing; he watched and could feel their breaths between kisses; he stared as his pulse became the thrusts of his pelvis while making love; then the beat became the blinking of her eyes, opening and closing with the rhythm of her heart, staring back at him as if she was there. He watched his pulse, and with every beat, a memory of her would flash in his mind until it seemed she was his very blood, coursing through his body in torrents of red and blue.

I like to believe there is a part of me that is always fully present to the moment wherever my mind may happen to be, preserving the truth of what is so that I may be able to look back on my life and speak of what was. This feature, of course, has no motive; nevertheless, it is the source of all memory, all life indeed, and I wish for nothing more than to accept this.

"How frustrating that there is always a remainder no matter how many answers we put on the table; there is always a factor, a question that never divides completely."

"Yes, but perhaps in that lies the secret?"

In love: almost impossible; in love: possible but difficult; in love: easy, but unlikely.

He looked in the backseat and saw his nephew with his eyes closed, feeling the breeze against his face as it rushed through the open car window. There was a smile on his lips, his head cocked gently to one side to catch the breeze and the rays of the sun. His uncle watched with joy to see the his nephew lost to a world of immediate perception, a world in which children find it so easy to live, a world that lends gravity to the imagination of each and every passing moment, straddling the universe of thought and sensation. He continued to watch. Eventually, his nephew opened his eyes and noticed his uncle watching. The boy simply smiled and fell back deeper into the car seat.

"You're really arrogant. You think you're so good-looking."

"Not true. I actually don't find myself good-looking at all, but I've accepted the fact, that for whatever reason, people find me attractive. Does this really make me a narcissist?"

I have always been vulnerable to women. But I am not a womanizer or a playboy. I'm not a rapist, a stalker, a heartbreaker, a pimp, a player, or a sex-addict. I am simply a person continuously under the spell of a woman's beauty, her charms, her graces, and her glories.

She thought of the way his body would continue to quake while still inside of her after climaxing, with heavy breaths, and sighs of total relaxation. Like the after shocks of an earthquake, his body would continue to shudder and shake, almost as if electricity was being shot through him.

"When he's inside of me, I know and feel how much he loves me because I can feel how much he surrenders, how much he opens up, how he gives his whole self to me; not out of a desire to possess or to take, but out of a passion to share who he is In those moments, I want nothing more than for him to remain inside of me, holding me close, for as long as heavenly possible."

She sat there on the bed by the window, smoking a cigarette, staring at the roses. They had been given to her weeks ago. Blood red and long stemmed, the roses had now shrunk, shriveled, and faded, but they still retained their beauty owing to the pure grace by which flowers age. She sat and stared longingly into them as if doing so might preserve them somehow.

"Are dead flowers really any less beautiful?" she thought. She looked away, out through the window, her thoughts turning toward him: where was he now? What was he doing? She could not bear to throw the flowers out; to do so would feel like throwing away a part of him.

She took another drag from her cigarette as she looked over her shoulder and on to the bed; his shirt was lying there, quietly, infused with his presence, motionless, as if it represented a funeral, his shirt taking the place of his body. She looked up from it and stared off into the corner of the room, into that open expanse that comprises the realm one calls space. Oh how she wished in that moment to be space itself, to be capable of manipulating it in order to bring him back for just another minute longer.

Lost in thought and daydreaming, he carelessly looked around, moving his eyes from the grass, to the birds, to the clouds; from the porch, to the house, to the pavement. Then his eyes landed on the large green leaves on the lawn. He looked up, realizing they had fallen from the big tree. It occurred to him that this tree was shedding leaves even though it was not fall. He watched the tree as another group of leaves fell from the top. Then he realized: trees shed their leaves in summer, not because they are dying, but because they are so filled with the sun that they are literally bursting with life. "This is how I want to live," he thought.

There were rows and rows of books, and so he picked one out at random, and casually leafed through it until he chanced upon a page with a short passage titled "What is a Relationship?" which read as follows:

"How is one to think of a relationship? It is certainly not about desperation, need, or necessity. It is not about becoming complete, feeling whole, or having company. It is not just about making a family or getting married because 'that's what people do.' What then is a relationship about? Is it an artistic statement, wanting to create something beautiful, wanting to participate in a process of expression and creation with another person; being the people we choose to be, having love for one's self, being comfortable enough to share who one knows themselves to be? Is love an art? It is certainly not an object, the man or woman not a brush, or a pen, not a tool. What then means 'a relationship'? – An act of being, expressing, experiencing, imagining, and creating together? Is it any wonder we call it 'making love?' One affirms themselves and then shares themselves with another. Is any of this true?"

He lifted his eyes from the page as people from both directions shuffled on past him down the aisle. He looked behind him, and then back in front, bracing himself for what he knew was about to be a moment of deep thought and reflection.

Such unpardonable destinies we rush to.

"You never have to fear losing the love of another. The reason is because the source of love, and the power of it, resides inside of you. It is sourced from how much you are willing to give and share and not how much you are able to take. But this can only occur when one is a complete human being, one loving enough of the very life one plans to share with another. Love and fear are antithetical."

She morphed into a cloud, floating in absence, through obscurity, no one there, and yet, there she remained.

"Your mind wants to put a thought to everything. It wants to be in control, the silly mind trying to put thoughts to feelings and experiences that can't be understood. Escape this and find peace."

Her eyes... How can I even begin to describe the feeling of looking into them?... Perhaps an analogy: I once went diving in Egypt in the Red Sea. Off the coast of the Sinai Peninsula by the town of Dahab is a "blue hole," a very deep expanse of water surrounded by a shallow expanse of sea. I remember walking over and into the blue hole, and that first look down into the water: this vast deep blue that went off into everything and nothing, it pulled me close. It just went on and on, there was no end to the beauty, I just stared and stared unable to take my eyes away, conscious of feeling overwhelmed by an unconscious being torn, peering into some deep mystery that was all its own; content in its essence that called for nothing, but said so much through a stillness unbeknown. I felt I could whisper to it, without the need to speak.

"Any advice?"

"Yes, know yourself; everything begins and ends with that."

"Don't worry, one day you'll look at your parents and realize that they practiced less than half of what they preached. You'll realize age is just a number, and that they had no idea what they were doing."

"I haven't been able to write anything for weeks."

"You know the best way to get over that kind of writer's block?"

"No, what?"

"Find a woman."

"It's strange, but I have a new relationship to memory, a relationship that is hard to describe. I'm very in touch with my memories, they arise very easily with much vividness, but they no longer feel like the past. Instead they feel like they are still happening, still relevant, even though the moments themselves have gone, even though I'm rooted in the present."

"It's as if you're running a race with millions of people. You are five miles ahead of everyone, but you're beating yourself up for not being ten miles ahead of everyone. Why can't you stop and give yourself credit for who you are and what you've done? Why can't you be content with that? Why can't you let go of this unquenchable desire to accomplish more than what is possible, more than would even make you happy?"

"He lived life unashamedly on his own terms, and whether we want to admit it or not, we were all jealous of him for doing so."

"You know what I'm sick of? I'm sick of everyone opening up their mouths and immediately giving an opinion when they hear some new idea, theory, or belief; without even giving a moment to really think about it, their minds are made up. Why can't people keep their mouths shut and just reflect on what was said without feeling the need to judge it so abruptly? If people were truly comfortable with whatever it is they think they know, and if they were concerned with truth more than with 'defending' their ideas, they would be a lot more patient in their listening."

That strange time of year when the seasons seemed locked in ambiguity, when spring can just as easily be fall and fall just as easily be spring; when one knows not whether spring is transitioning to summer, or fall transitioning to winter; when the cool crisp breezes of morning and night make it so, leaving one unsure where one is or where one is going, fooling one into thinking there is a choice in the matter; perhaps stemming from the seasons themselves, who, aware of the seeming lull between time, gain the desire to move from spring to winter or from fall to summer, all the while knowing, deep down, that such choices are impossible.

The transition on his face from frown to smile was so extreme and so intense that one cold go temporarily mad if caught staring between the two.

It was perhaps the most charming place I had ever visited; to take out my camera and try to capture its beauty would have been a disservice, not just to the beauty of the landscape, but to myself self for not knowing better.

Yet now, as I write this, I realize that perhaps I too lack the same humility for trying to write about it. But wait, perhaps I am engaged in something different, for there is nothing I can capture, only experiences that I can translate.

All the same, many of the houses were crumbling before my eyes, but with a humility so admirable, it was if the slope of the house, resulting from years of slow erosion, was some cordial or reverential bow by the house to the ravages of time, a bow that acknowledged the futility of trying to stand on solid ground forever. I swear the house was smiling at its eventual fate.

There is something in a flower that keeps it beautiful, even after it dies, when its leaves have shriveled and its colors have faded.

"Childhood is universally regarded as the happiest time in one's life, and yet we all have to grow up. What was it about childhood that made it so great?"

"I'm not sure it was. As a kid, all I wanted to do was to grow up. I thought I could do whatever I wanted once I was older."

"Yea, that's true. If only it was possible to go be a child again, but this time with the wisdom of knowing better."

He stood looking at the aisles and aisles of books in rows and rows stacked neatly on the shelves; many of these books he had read, many he had not, and many he never would. He had heard of people who, in their quest for personal truth and self-understanding, had burned their books, or even thrown them in a river in a bout of frustration or conviction. Such an act was one he knew he would never do, but he felt great respect and sympathy for those who did. He could remember times when he thought about what it would be like to have read everything, only to realize that it would essentially amount to very little, when he would ask himself, "Cannot everything be found from within?" And yet, he continued to read and read a lot, sometimes five or six books at a time.

He sat there holding the rock, observing it with wonder. Walking up from behind was a friend of his father's.

"Yep, simple minds are impressed by simple things," he said.

"What's so simple about a rock," the boy retorted.

The older man stood there as the boy looked up at him with a fierce and disparaging look.

"A rock is millions and millions of years old. It is comprised of thousands of elements and took ages to become as hard as it is. Only a simple mind would see this rock as something simple and insignificant instead of being marveled by it for the miracle that it is."

The older man was in no way prepared for such a response, and so he just stood there trying not to look as if he had been affected; stood there trying to maintain the image of the "all knowing" adult.

"Isn't it amazing how you can feel so at home in places that are so far away?"

"Maybe we lived here in past lives?"

"I don't know."

"Maybe there comes a point where one lives a life where one becomes obsessed with travel and the whole point is to go and visit all those places one lived in the past. Maybe it is an important step before one can go to the next life where one is more spiritually advanced or something."

"Yea, that sounds pretty crazy, but interesting, who knows."

How distressing that your sanctuary can easily become your prison, when you go from feeling the comforts associated with having a place to yourself, where your entire being is free to flow out in expression, to feeling trapped and helpless as if all of who you are has turned against you. When does this happen? It happens when you spend too much time in one place, when you stand in opposition to the immutability of the living universe; it happens when certain memories keep you bogged down in the mire of regret, and when you can sense the winds of fortune start to blow your way, beckoning you to share your spirit with the wider world.

The silence of the landscape

Have you ever watched your various memories turn from good or bad before your very eyes as a result of whatever fortunes or misfortunes happened to occur in a given moment? It's amazing how a memory that was once a joy becomes sad and distasteful because of some chance happenings. For instance, when you're in love and everything is fine, all of your memories bring you great pleasure. But if things turn sour then so do the memories associated with the person you loved.

Those songs you wish went on forever; should we hold those who wrote them accountable for not composing more, or should we belittle ourselves for not thinking them perfect?

"Look at my hands. You'd think I never worked a day in my life. But they've been put through a lot. I don't know why they're so soft."

"I don't know how else to describe the feeling other than to say that when I stood there, up on the hill, overlooking the water, it was if the sea was inside of me, I could feel the sea inside of me."

"Yeah, but he's just one of those people that everything works out for; it doesn't matter what happens, things just go his way."

He has a look that makes it seem as if part of him is always connected to another world, as if there is one foot planted here and the other planted in some other realm: the realm of fate, the realm of afterlife; I don't know.

"I refuse to believe we're a tragedy."

"How can you say something so cliché? You're a poet."

"Exactly! As a poet it's my job to honor and pay respect to those great lines that are still meaningful."

"I bet you give long-stemmed red roses to your girlfriend as well."

"Absolutely! There will never be a more beautiful flower. A cliché become cliché for a reason. You know I'm not sure I can ever love a woman who doesn't like roses."

And so I search for the source of that feeling, finding it somewhere at the center of a great pulsation, where the light of the universe refracts through an open stretch of darkness, a vast expanse that has lost any and all characteristics for the sake of transcendence.

He could feel his unconscious swirl in rhythm to a deep vibration somewhere in the pit of his abdomen, at the center of his being.

"What if I told you that you would be married your whole life to a man who never once told you that he loved you?"

He didn't realize what his words were doing to her, how every time he said her name, another drop of water fell into some great ocean, drowning her in a torrent from whose depths she would never escape.

He loved her with his whole being. She knew it, and that's why it hurt her so much.

And let it remain and never flinch from the left and broken crest of a life given till dusk. Let dawn harass the darkness until it gives into the light of morning. And from it, allow living its due course of movement through the unimpeded so that it never reaches.

"You're just like most men, 'manly' enough to date and fuck a woman, but not strong or brave enough to truly love her."

"Let her find her way to you."

"You have to let those voices speak, let them be heard despite any doubts or apprehensions on the part of you or others. Do not discount them for they are real, whether you think they spring purely from your imagination or from somewhere else."

She was gone now, but his memories were so painfully vivid; they conjured up her ghost around the buildings, along the pathways and sidewalks, in the forest, and on the hills across the fields.

The path went by her room, the path he had to walk everyday to get to town. He walked the path daily, and every time he approached her building, his heart would pound, his stomach would drop, and his eyes would try and shoot out from their sockets toward its direction. He always looked, and it always made him feel, and the feeling always made him think, and his thoughts always made him wonder, and his wonder always made him afraid, afraid he had lost her. And with this, the challenge of feeling love at its extreme limits became a delicate test of teetering on the brink of sanity, unsure of whether the disintegration of his mind that seemed to be taking place was, at heart, some divine and cleansing purgation, or the effect of some disastrous misfortune to his psyche, or both.

"I had a boring life. I was too afraid to do anything."

The place is under a large tree, a tree that is said to be over one thousand years old, a tree so old that it was alive and breathing before the first crusade had been declared, before the Byzantine Empire had even begun its slow decline. This tree carries its large protruding roots and large sways of wrinkly bark in a dignified, honorable, humble, and yet proud way, like a grandmother or grandfather. I say "grandmother" and "grandfather" instead of any old person in general to emphasize the kind of I energy I feel emanates from this tree whenever I am around or touching it. It has a soft, soothing energy, warm and loving. Sometimes, if I have a sore muscle or some ache in my body, I'll place my hands up against her and ask for her energy to heal me. Whenever I do. I feel better.

There is a large split on the side of the tree where, at one point, a large branch or chunk of the tree had been broken off during a storm, struck by lightning, leaving large splinters of wood that now resembled giant toothpicks. Yet she bears these scars with honor and humility, reminding me of how gracefully it is possible to age.

In the tree are squirrels that chew on the tree's acorns, often dropping them onto the yoga platform. During yoga, one can often hear them falling down around one's self, and yet neither I nor any student has been hit, which reinforces my affections for and belief that this tree is watching over me like a grandmother.

The woods surrounding this place, especially up on the hill by the yoga platform, gives off a hot breeze that smells like burned pine and dry grass. It is a smell so undeniably similar to the forests of South Carolina, more specifically, from my time at Parris Island that I sometimes

find myself to be in two places at once, and oddly enough,
I don't seem to mind.

"For me one of the most important things was to realize that life has no time limits, there is no list of things that must be "checked off," there is no final destination. You have to live without a care for where you end up or how you get there. You have to be present, content with the simple feeling of being alive, and when you do this, time will slowly come to halt; you'll be puzzled by the dissidence of your momentum, wondering how it is to go on after revolting, having thrown off the chains of your own impulses. But you'll breathe again, only this time each breathe will ground you more firmly and with ever deeper roots into the constancy of the all pervading moment."

The extreme limits of love: where a person no longer lives, but only because life has returned home.

"I don't know what's happened but my memories have become extremely vivid recently. It is no exaggeration to say that when a particular memory is stirred inside of me I literally find myself transported back to the event. I say 'to the event' instead of back through time because these experiences make time seem nonexistent or simply irrelevant, and I'm not sure what it all means."

"My throat trembled, my jaw twitched. I looked a bit closer and felt my eyes swell. I braced for my pulse, for my heart to pound harder. I clenched the cuffs of my shirt and took in a deeper breath. I shut my eyes, removed my glasses, and felt the tears begin to roll down my face."

How does one survive the challenges associated with the mysteries of life? By that I mean the great wonders and the unfathomable beauty that survives without reason or a lasting explanation, always as an incomplete answer, like a divided number with a constant remainder. Do we survive by taking pleasure in the mystery itself, finding peace in the fact that it is a mystery with no complete answer? By indulging in the mystery, by accepting that unanswerable quality as somehow the source of its majesty? What is an answer after all? Does knowing how a flower grows increase the splendor of watching it bloom?

He was an incredibly sensitive soul. If you ever sat and just looked at him for a long period of time, it was like he was carrying the weight of the entire world's emotions. You could look into his eyes and see the entire world, all the pain and suffering, but all the pleasure and joy as well.

Most people run from that kind of sensitivity. He never did, but it took its toll, and I'm sure that more than once, he regretted and hated how sensitive he was. But he never betrayed it because he knew it would be a lie.

"Ask yourself what inspires awe, and reflect on it; reflect and pursue the origin of that feeling to its conception. Go deeper, and explore the depths until the source of all that brings wonder divulges its secrets. Look closely with the certainty of a mirror, and never be afraid to feel at one with what you find; do not doubt it."

He did not want to live, but he did not want to die; he wanted be alive and to feel life, and for that reason, living, living in a way connected with the expectations and norms of society, felt pointless, unreal, like the life of a mannequin.

"Why live when one can be alive? Yes exactly!" he thought.

His mind could not avoid the fact that they weren't together, and so with every thought, another drop fell into some great pool of sorrow that seemed to stretch out and into the oblivions of a thousand quaking heartbeats, pulsing with the force of a great constancy, where the perception of a different truth made it sting and hurt, but, fortunately, with good cause.

"You focus only the fact that you're not together. You never stop to remember the rest of the details. If you did, you would know that everything is fine. You focus on the difficulties of being together, but you don't focus on what she's done, how she confessed her love for you, how she gave you as much as she could, even at the cost of so much suffering. You forget what you mean to her, how she misses you, that she may feel more afraid and vulnerable than you can possibly imagine. You love her, I know, but you need to hold fast to everything you both have shared together and find solace in some eternity of it."

Persevere, and I promise that one day your greatest weakness will become your greatest strength, your greatest loss your biggest gain, and your biggest fear your greatest teacher.

If only it wasn't such a struggle to give one's feelings a home, somewhere inside. Feelings should be welcomed into one's life to live comfortably along side one's self, instead of being treated like some flatmate reluctantly allowed to live with you for the sake of cheaper rent.

Have you ever stood by a tree in a city and had the sense that it did not want to be there, having to watch its leaves fall onto some black pavement or some slab of solid sidewalk? Perhaps it stares at the surrounding buildings decorated in plastered vines and molded flowers, holding their creators in contempt for what must seemingly be the gravest of insults to its own nature.

"Has it ever occurred to you that she may have given and expressed to you everything she was capable of? Her limits are not your limits. She may have stretched herself to the edge, perhaps gone beyond it, beyond what she was able to do. If so, then what more can you ask? Have you done the same?"

At the intersection of what is and what it means to be

"I was walking through the city. I passed an older woman with a sallow face, and exhausted eyes. She bore the look of quiet desperation. Seeing her, it dawned on me that everyone is trying their best with what they have, doing the most with what they can to live a happy life. After that, looking around, for some reason, everyone I saw became more beautiful."

"I have this irresistible urge to experience the world, to get to know it on the most intimate of levels, to feel life as deep as possible. I want to remove any barrier that keeps me from feeling close to the universe at its very core, to its source."

"I fell in love at first sight. I know such a thing is possible because I know such a thing happened. I know what I saw when I looked into her eyes. And I know what I felt. I find it impossible to describe either, and for me, that gives the experience more validity, and grants it reality."

I lay on the floor. Suddenly it felt like my body was a mound, under the soil and covered in earth. From out of this mound grew flowers whose roots were underground, tangled up with my body, growing from my organs. From underground, I could perceive the flowers, I could feel their bloom, feel them grow, feel them age as if through seasons. I felt and became these flowers dying, withering and crimping until they laid low. And then suddenly, a tree burst from the mound, rising into the air fully grown with huge robust limbs and a solid trunk. The flowers were the source of this new life; my organs were the source of it, and it grew from my body.

"I remember thinking that wisdom would remove ignorance from my life, but it only makes ignorance stand out more. What a fool I was to search for wisdom, thinking it would dispel the ignorance from my life. I now know that in finding wisdom, ignorance will stand out more clearly, and in so doing, tempt me to play a kind of "fool's game" to destroy it."

To watch the tenacity of life; the way one can look at the side of a barren cliff and see one plant or flower that found way a to live, stuck between solid rock, growing from the tiniest of crevices with only a speck of soil to sustain it.

I looked into her eyes and felt the overwhelming power of attraction, not just of my attraction to her, the power that was compelling me towards her, but of attraction itself. I felt that very source of power that exhorts one thing toward another, that powerful energy that impels life into existence; one can see it in the way a plant angles itself toward the sun's light, or the way a flower comes into bloom, not for any ultimate purpose, but rather just to be; because life is all the more beautiful precisely because it has no motives.

Incited to feel the heart of attraction itself, lofted into the realm of a source found past to nowhere; moving beyond to a place without motive; leaving intention itself behind?

He sat there bathed in clouds of smoke, with the light of the sun refracting through the second story porch windows and into...

"There is no ultimate purpose dependent on things existing, as opposed to not existing. When one looks at the trees, rivers, oceans, planets, stars, sun, and moon, one realizes that there is no need for any of it, and yet they are. There is no need for any of it, and yet they exist. There is no true meaning, but perhaps that is what makes everything more wondrous. All things will eventually pass away, and yet all things are.

I can still remember the day I found out that I would eventually die. I was a small boy. I was at my aunt's house, and there was a movie on where one of the characters was having a discussion with her relative about death. I don't remember exactly what transpired, but I remember asking my aunt if I would one day die too. She said, "Yes" and I began crying. But in not too much time, I got over it.

As years passed by, I became interested in that incident, and I began asking myself what made me continue to go on despite knowing that it would all come to an end. Surely, the realization of death was an intense experience for me, but how was it not completely devastating, devastating to the point where living any longer felt pointless?"

I can't stop thinking of you, and how I'm willing to do almost anything to be with you. Then I realize that it's not just what I want and am willing to do. I'm realizing that more important than having you is having loved you in the first place. I love you with such an incomprehensible tenacity. I'm happy and thankful for the entire experience. Loving you has been my greatest adventure. I'm realizing that moving on doesn't have to mean no longer loving.

Have you approached the bareness? A kind of skulking before the spirit, amongst the living, yet beyond the stubborn soul, where indifference pries itself into one's instincts in order to go on living; marching down on the thunder claps of hesitancy with a wide open determination, vast enough to incorporate their power; obsessive enough to continue moving forward?

Just this once, give up all your memories and embrace the sensation of the ever present void, that "blank check" of creation, dashing itself upon the shores of discernment, not as a conqueror, but as an all-pervading "what will be," a kind of sempiternal foundation upon which an eternity of constructions may lay themselves. It does justice to life, as much as you believe the opposite. If you could but draw reality from the figure of your imagination.

I could feel my inner adversary warning me through eyes of blotted fire, reminding me of the consequences of failure; wielding guilt – that conjoined bastard twin of the self, congealed to one's better half – and cutting through like a scythe across my gut, the sound of an echo whispering the futility in triumph, slicing through my bowels. How would any success ever be enough. And yet, to give up – give up what?

My entire past is rushing into my present life to be burned as an offering for all that I still must do, and all that remains to be done.

Dashed to pieces against the shores of an arrogant sublimity parading itself down the vaulted corridors of my inner palace – only in my mind, only in thought was my reason on firm ground. Were such thoughts to venture from the premises and step out into the gilded world, they would find themselves stranded and, what's worse, for a mind mired in self-adulation (as all minds are), completely worthless.

All my reasons, my foolproof arguments, and landlocked excuses; all my hardness, my determination; all my grit. From just one glance, all was shattered upon seeing her again. One look and my gut swelled with desire, the way the sky swells with light from the sun as it makes its first nod above the horizon. How does a forest fire begin from a spark? It seems impossible, does it not? But then it happens.

"I fell in love with her soul the moment I saw her. How can I just walk away from that?"

That moment on the cusp of death, when the last glimmerings of life pulse through the echoes of soul; it is said that at such a moment all of one's life will flash before one's eyes. Will we get the chance to linger at any of our memories?

"Sometimes I think about a certain woman I loved; I made love to her with such passion and intensity; I think of how I gave my soul and surrendered everything to those moments. Then I wonder if it's possible to every truly love another woman again after that. Surely, I will try, and surely, it will be enjoyable to find out. But I also fear never knowing such love again."

God, I have fallen for this woman so deeply. Perhaps I allowed myself to look too far into her eyes. Surely that is the cause. There is so much in her eyes. There is something very precious, very profound. It's not just their beauty; it's the soul I can see behind them.

"I can't help it! I want to tell you how special you are. I'm not a fool. I know what you mean to me. I know when I'm in the midst of beauty of soul, and I feel incredibly lucky to have been permitted to stare so deeply into your eyes and have a glimpse."

What I find disheartening is that, in all truth, I cannot look into my own child's eyes and tell her life is worth living. Thankfully, she has yet to concern herself with such matters. So then I must have hope and find the purpose to keep going. I must find some kind of peace, some kind of answer that can sit comfortably afloat, atop the depths of the existential ocean, so that one day, when the challenges and enigmas of life weigh her down through an insufferable sinking, she may come to me with a comment or a question such as "Why is life so painful?" or say "I don't want to go on living," and I may be able to confidently look her in the eyes and say, "No! Life IS worth living; keep going, my dear child, and you will find what it is you are searching for." And this comment will not be THE answer, and I doubt it will be met with much optimism. But it will be enough to give her hope that perseverance has an end, and, most importantly, she will know she is not alone.

One day, on the verge of death, the entirety of my life will flash before my eyes. As it does, there will be moments, moments I will attempt to prolong and sustain, even if for just a microsecond longer: memories of first loves and first kisses; memories of profound insight; memories of serenity with nature; and the most blessed memory of all, time spent with my grandma in her kitchen, cooking with her and being fed by her loving hands.

The patience with which he heard her speak to her child was enough to impress upon him the conviction that here was a woman confident enough to give all that she could without expectation of anything in return; there was no residue of burden whatsoever placed upon her son that might make him feel responsible for his mother's happiness or self-worth. Here was devotion given life and made manifest, away from the hollow talk of good intentions and exalted promises, speech which counts for nothing until animated by the moment-to-moment sacrifice that constitutes the worship of living love.

Of course, I cannot be sure, but I suspect I never wanted to be born. I think of past lives and imagine that my last one ended after a long period of suffering through which I managed, with great perseverance, to find some semblance of peace and depart from this world without a grudge toward the maker, or to life.

I have heard it said that when one dies, one enjoys respite in another realm from where one actively begins planning one's next life so as to continue to pay off the karmic debt accrued through many lives caught up within the great muses of cause and effect.

I imagine that I was not eager to plan, but by the fact that I am here, plan I did. I reluctantly settled on a plan, but was desperate not to have to carry it out. Perhaps God himself had to give me encouragement.

I can imagine myself talking to him and saying, "Why must I go back? I relinquish it all. Turn me to nothing: no memory, no semblance of spirit."

"Such a thing cannot be done," he would reply.

And so he conveys it to me that there is only one direction in which a person can move, and that all beings slowly converge towards the pinnacle of celestial being, until they reach it.

Oh, sweet Divinity, when may I go back to floating adrift on the cosmic ocean, in oblivion, surrounded by hemispheres of divine love and horizons of everlasting light?

I saw these two birds in a cage and couldn't help but envy them. What a wonderful and easy life, I thought. But then I stared a little longer and noticed the wings; I remembered what wings are for. I realized I could never be a caged bird, no matter how easy and wonderful the life, no matter how kind the caretaker. I would need to fly, even though it meant flying headlong into a world filled with dangers, inconveniences, and difficulties. What about the sky and the open freedom of being?

What a struggle it has been to find truth. If only finding it was the end of the journey. Unfortunately, the real test is to live it. Truth, meaning, all the mystery, we discovered it a long time ago; we know the answers to the questions we labor over, we simply don't like them. It seems half of life involves discovering the truth; the other half involves finding the courage to live it.

My things became objects, and these objects became "people," and these "people" would not love me. I stretched my imagination and harassed my dreams until they conformed to a slumbering reality lulling itself to sleep, constructing and building, just so I could snooze a little longer.

"You know what? I have no reason to a read another book the rest of my life. I think we continue to read so that we don't have to live the wisdom found in the books we already read."

"Why do you need to go there? You know, if you keep looking for danger, eventually it will find you."

"Just give yourself permission."

"Permission to do what?"

"Permission to live in the moment, for the sake of yourself, without wondering about what you think you owe to the world or what you think it wants from you."

"Nature can seem so sinister at times, but what does it say about us that we always want to talk about its disasters as if they are created with malicious intent? Does it somehow make us more comfortable to turn disaster into an adversary? Is it too painful a thought to simply accept that nature acts indiscriminately and without reason? Fire burns, waters flood, wind sways; why do we have to talk about these things as if they are people? The howling wind, the relentless waves, the menacing fire; we have to make everything familiar. Is that what we're doing?"

He thought that he might be too deep, that no one would dare to venture to such depths just to understand someone else, to dive fearlessly towards the deepest part of the human ocean consisting of desires, fears, and confusions, simply out of love. But she said she would happily dive, that she looked forward to it. He felt skeptical, but when he saw the look in her eyes, he noticed a willingness born of light that was guiding her way through his inner maze.

"At best, all one can be is a lighthouse to the world, a kind of guide; the ocean of life, with its tumult and turmoil will always be there. You are stranded in your own boat, forced to strain, and only you can guide yourself to shore safely. You're only a beacon of light for others' orientation. Tend your light. That is your one and only responsibility."

Just realize your image will never do justice to your self, your words will never adequately capture your feelings, your ideas can never be understood, and your experiences can't be explained.

"You don't go mad from experiencing something, whether the experience is divine or tragic. You go mad from trying to comprehend it. You can only experience the incomprehensible. You'll lose yourself trying to explain it."

This acclimation of mind is a painful thing. One gets used to the cacophony of life, its endless parade of noises and distractions. When you sit silently and allow them to cease, you start going mad. Stay in your suffering long enough, and it will become too uncomfortable to leave. It will come to wear you, and you'll spend your life justifying it. Your suffering is just clothing that you are free to discard at anytime, but you wear it like it's your skin.

She finished speaking.

He waited at the table for a double-dealing with himself. There could be no more struggling, no more rationalizations. Intuitively knowing this would be the end, he let his hands fall on the table, fingers folded, staring into his other self. "You don't have to speak to her."

His self understood and relented, saying nothing, but comprehending; their eyes "shook" on it.

Thus one self spoke to another; he communicated to himself what he needed to hear.

He said nothing back to her, and it all ended; their involvement was through.

"When did everything become so serious?"

"Yes, before everything became serious. When was that?"

"Don't worry. I know that suicidal feeling. Do not be ashamed of it. You are not mad. It is the logical conclusion of a reflective life where one sheds the skin of false identity, of values that were chosen for you, not by you, of being in awe of the mystery of life, its seeming pointlessness, and the head-banging symphony that resounds from trying to think through it all. Embrace the ideation for what it is, but do not give in. There is a light at the end of this tunnel, though you cannot yet see it. And that's the point."

"What's so unsettling about the present!?! I just can't stay here!"

"Can you keep pace with your own footsteps? It's a weird question, I know, but if you pay attention, you'll notice how difficult you'll find it just to walk with yourself. Your pace can't keep up with your mind. But it's your mind that should be "walking" with your pace. That's where the difficulty lies."

Who would have thought that now, even with time passed and years between us, in my spare moments of quiet and ease, rounded out from the frantic pace of the day, that my mind seamlessly drifts to thoughts of you: the memory of your eyes, the taste of your lips, my hands running through your hair, the sound of your voice, the touch of your body. I find myself randomly speaking your name in such moments, late at night, hoping to conjure up your being from the fog of memory and the breath that must be spoken, even if no one is around to hear it.

"Life must either be a frightful dream or a cruel prank. Maybe a sick joke? Perhaps all three? At different times?"

"I think it's more like a harmless goof. It's just play."

"You don't think it's cruel?"

"No. It just seems that way because we take things too seriously."

"Can you live with not knowing? The mind tells you that you can't. The mind cannot know what a greater part of you understands. A greater part of you knows something that the mind never will."

I saw a bee that had been wounded. It was stuck in a long corridor, struggling to fly normally, the way it had always known. It would fly up and then sputter off before crashing into the stone wall and falling back down to the ground. I could feel the confusion of the bee, it's fear, how desperately it wanted to simply fly again. Something about the perseverance and futility stung me deeply. The simultaneity widened the opening to the great precipice and void of human questioning, where we wonder about the way lives are taken from this planet. But I like to think this precipice is not a trap, that it somehow holds the answer.

Here is the real point of logic and reason: the logical conclusion to be drawn from logic and reason is that logic and reason are limited; they are limited in their ability to give sufficient explanation and answer to our sense of wonder and our deepest and most puzzling questions.

"I traveled to see the world. But of equal importance is traveling so as to allow the world to see me. That's why I plan to leave again."

Would you wait patiently, watching some sweet liquor drip slowly, drop by drop, from the heavens, into your own personal cup of life, over the course of a lifetime, if it meant having the sweetest and most sustaining drink? Think about such a task, and think deeply. None of this seems worth it because you haven't yet tasted the liquor. But that is not the problem. We cannot possibly know what it is we are searching for.

Do you ever wonder what the world does when no one is around to observe it, how the trees move, how the birds sing, how the grass grows. I'm not sure what it is, but it brings me peace to imagine nature when I leave it alone. When we leave this patch of woods, the trees will still be here swaying, growing, taking in the sun's light. It seems to speak to something eternal, some perennial truth in us all.

He looked back and replied, "Well, I've never considered myself to be a lazy person, but unmotivated? Yes, that's definitely been me. But how much is actually worth being motivated for? I can't help it that most things are pointless. There are plenty of things I love working hard for; they're just not the things for which society wants me to be motivated."

There are times when, no matter how large it may seem in actuality, the whole of the world feels like a box, a prison, a cocoon, a padded room, and you can't stand being in it. And there are times when your home, no matter how small, cheap, or insignificant, feels like the whole of the universe, with you at the center of it; your sanctuary.

"I know there's a wellspring of unconditional joy and ecstasy somewhere in the pit of my body. Of its own accord, it bubbles up to a higher order. I know that people think that all joy and happiness must be dependent on some thing out there, some causal relation, but that's the mind's expectation. I sense the truth and do not need an answer."

"No one understands me. No one ever has. That's the lamentable part. I want to believe that the liberating thought is knowing it does not matter. Who else can understand one's self? It feels great being understood, but truly and honestly, does that ever happen? Is it supposed to happen? Sympathized and empathized with, yes, but understood? Only I stand under myself, not by choice. And that is the way it ought to be."

"The grace by which some older women age and carry themselves is beyond intoxicating."

There is a great stream that flows through the center at the source of all things, moving to the rhythm of a great pulsation.

Do you ever notice the way children stare? How they stop and look at you so unashamedly, fearlessly, unintimidated. There's no hesitancy, just a strong desire to explore, see the world, and simply be with it.

"What am I actually searching for?"

"I've found it terribly hard to let go of my perfectionism, of having to be the best. And how can I? If everything I do has to be the best, then that includes being the best at letting go. I've never been able to break this cycle. All of my trying is laced with perfectionism, guilt, and slave driving myself, even when I'm not supposed to try."

"Yes, I can see your dilemma. Consider that you've created the conflict by asking the question. If the question is paradoxical and presents an irresolvable problem then the question doesn't serve you. This does not negate the problem, however. Can you stay with the task without turning it into a question for your mind? No answer, no question, just being with what you see and feel?"

"Good morning, grass. Look at you, being beautiful, shining in the sun, not trying to be the best grass. Just being, and being all the more splendid because of it."

"I had to look at the picture of myself as a baby, with those gleaming eyes and a smile that seemed to push to the ends of the earth. What happened to that child? What happened to the light that once shone from those eyes, eyes that glistened like large drops of rain sitting on a blade of grass? Do I still have that light? Do the pools of my sight still shimmer? Is that bursting smile still there, or have those mountains of cheek and dimple crumbled away forever, spilled over into an ocean of everlasting despair?"

"You can never pull your intentions out from the heart and show it to the world as proof of what you intended. Can you accept that?"

"What bothers me is the hurry and the pace at which we live. We rush through life, creating unpardonable destinies, and then we get to the end, and want it all back."

It can be a terribly painful experience sitting in front of some beautiful landscape, trying to take it all in. I suspect that the pain comes from that very act, trying to take it all in, to process it all, like the world is some set of puzzle pieces that can be ordered into something clear and linear. Staring out upon a beautiful sunset or prairie or summit view can induce the right kind of insanity, one that breaks the desire for comprehension, the way a koan breaks one's reason; a madness that dispels madness.

Awe, contentment, truth…

He stood over his child, watching her as she slept. Then he gently began to whisper, "I promise to always support you. To be there for you when you need to be comforted. To be there for you when you are in doubt. To be there when you need someone to hold you. To be there when you need someone to laugh with, someone to listen, someone to hate, someone to vent to. I promise never to make you feel like a burden, and to love you without condition."

"Do you know why some great minds go mad?"

"No."

"They get a glimpse of some ineffable truth that swells their being with joy and all-pervasiveness. Then they try and put it into words, into logic, and into reason. They go insane from trying to make sense of it, trying to put awe, the infinite, the ecstatic, into a box to have it organized and controlled."

"I do not wish to go mad."

"Yes, but an encounter with madness is inevitable, especially for those inclined to ask heartbreakingly difficult questions in the hope of discovering freedom, truth, and love."

"No, it is much simpler. Do what you want, don't feel shame, and be open to change. Those are my commandments."

"Keep in mind, when I say I am a student of poetry I mean I am a student of poetry herself, not a student of poetry, the literary style, or of poets."

"The longer I live, the more life feels like a dream."

"What would we do without our enemies? We completely underestimate how happy we are to have them in our lives: people to dislike, to hate, to argue against; people to be bear the brunt of our repressed aggressions as well as to make us feel we are and seem better. We don't want our enemies gone or to change as much as we pretend to believe; we have enemies, and we are glad they are there."

The raindrops quietly falling into pools of water, gently percussing waves to the end of a silence that has no beginning; but the pulsing vibrations, echoing movements of the infinite, never was, happening, always.

"We all know someone like that, right? They're just lucky. The Gods or the 'Fates' just seem to love them. Why?"

"I'd say because of how he lives. If I had to guess, it's because of his passion for life and experiencing the world. The world loves his love for it; the world is addicted to his passion and appreciation. The world – all the trees, flowers, plants, animals, even the food, the drinks – it all resonates to his love. He loves experiencing the world, and the world, in turn, loves being experienced by him."

"Can you feel that sense of panic in the face of the unknown? That desperate grabbing for something amidst the fall, though there is nothing to be held? It is not the unknown that frightens; it is not the awe that feels overwhelming. That disturbing, unnerved feeling is the mind afraid of not being in control, of not understanding when faced with the prospect of surrendering to the ineffable."

Oh, Cupid! Please shoot this woman. Shoot as her eyes are locked with mine. It is due justice for the soul she is stealing from me!

"You know how some people are one way in public and then completely different behind closed doors? I can't stand it. I like him because he's the same whether in private or public. I hate that kind of dishonest formality of snake and skin-shedding common with so many people; that weaving of a tapestry made from the thread of dead puppets. I will always trust and admire the honest criminal, villain, and vagabond over the phony and sanctimonious 'saint' and do-gooder."

"What do you think happens when you die?"

"It is very much like sleep at first: you slowly drift off; things go black. Everything and everyone is gone. You cannot see anything, but you know there is some kind of movement occurring. Then things open up quietly, in the deepest of silences. You begin traversing through space and light, eventually ending up at a Sun. It is there that you will experience a great knowing, like watching your entire life just spent as if it were a movie, except it will flash before you in an instant, and you will reflect on it with others from that life. You will meet your guides."

"In my reflections, I have discovered a deep-seated fear of the very happiness I seek. It is a fear of happiness, of peace, of stillness, but most of all, of contentment.

"Contentment?" it asks in astonishment and trepidation. "And give up desire? No more striving for exotic faraway lands, beautiful women, or enchanting objects!"

The fear cannot imagine because it has never known a life without such things, the trying and the attainment. This fear is justified, to a point. How can one strive for something one has never known and cannot even imagine? Contentment? To be content with always being discontent? It seems that is the best one can do, does it not? But contentment must exist; otherwise, why the fear? Fear refuses to imagine. It refuses to imagine, and what it can imagine cannot be free of what it knows. It knows striving, and so it must take a leap of reason, and catch up with the rest of me."

Every step garners me the life that is living itself perpetually without my knowing. So what do I know? Very little it seems.

About

Mark is a student of philosophy, poetry, psychoanalysis, religion, somatics, and Russian literature. His passions include color, light, beauty, breath, silence, love, truth, tea, riding horses, playing the drums, doing yoga and smoking a good cigar. A Marine Corps veteran, Mark has a Bachelors degree in philosophy from the University at Buffalo, and a Masters in Counseling Psychology from Pacifica Graduate Institute. Fond of travel, he has visited, lived, and volunteered in a number of countries. He currently resides in Santa Barbara California, but perpetually lives in Buffalo, NY. He maintains a blog and website with many other forms of his writing at zmanmark.com.

Made in the USA
Middletown, DE
02 March 2019